THE LONG FOREST TRAIL

Story by: Clay Vilhauer & Amber Vilhauer
Illustrated by: Andres Meneses

Published and distributed by STRONGPrint Publishing
Colorado, USA

Library of Congress Control Number: 2023919234
Vilhauer, Clay and Vilhauer, Amber
The Long Forest Trail
ISBN: 978-1-962074-07-0

STRONGPrint
PUBLISHING

To adults and kids around the world.

Be the light.

"Be the light" means choosing to make the world a happier place.
It's about focusing on what you can control—your thoughts (mindset)
and feelings inside.

When you feel good inside,
it spreads happiness and brightness to people around you,
like sharing a big smile or a warm hug.

Not long ago, on the last days of Fall,
Clay and his mom answered nature's own call.

Hand held in hand, down the long forest trail,
together, as always, the two couldn't fail.

Reaching a river,
they spread lunch with care,
while butterflies danced
around in the air.

Mom asked Clay questions
to get him to think.
"What makes you happy,
and what makes you shrink?"

"I shrink and feel sad
when the dark side comes in.
It doesn't last long
when I imagine it spin.

Hard feelings spin
into a true joyful space.
This is the space
I call my Happy Place.

I'm happy when I think
of what I'm grateful for,
like Mom and Dad,
home, travel, and more."

Leaves gently dropped
as they went on their way,
showing nature's lessons
to accept change each day.

Just then, buzzed a mosquito
—*his bite strong although small*—
teaching Clay, through challenge,
you still can stand tall.

"Why does the world
have bad things?!"
Clay cried.

"To help make us strong,"
Mom said, feeling great pride.

"We always keep going,
keep moving," she shared.
"Mindset matters most
when life seems unfair."

The two kept on hiking;
then out of the blue,
    Mom asked, "Is your bug bite
    still bothering you?"

    "Not anymore!" Clay said,
    feeling great cheer.
    "See?" Mom said,
    "Things do get better,
    my dear!"

    "Life's worries
    are like bug bites
        eager to stay—
        with time, feelings fade,
        moving out of our way.

    Frustrations get better,
    annoyance takes flight,
    leaving us happy
    and feeling just right!"

Winter arrived
with its snowflakes big and white.
The two walked and talked,
holding each other tight.

A dog appeared
along their path one day
wearing a cozy coat
to keep cold at bay.

"Love Puppy,"
read his collar tag bright;
he'd lost his way
but found warmth that night.

"He's lost!" Clay cried out,
filled with worry inside.
"We're better together,"
Mom smiled and replied.

With peanut butter
and fresh water to spare,
their kindness showed Clay
it's important to care.

The cold snow continued;
Clay pushed through the slush,
asking, "Mom,
why *do* you like nature so much?"

"When life's pressures build,
nature keeps me connected.
I find that my fear
is less big than expected.

I look at the world
and find wisdom around.
It reminds me how to go
from lost back to found."

Spring arrived,
possibility filled the air.
Flowers bloomed,
and leaves sprouted with care.

A small, playful squirrel
danced from tree to tree,
inspiring the others
to run and be free.

The trail's end was near
and their walks almost done;

"What did we learn?"
Mom asked, enjoying the sun.

"To show love and trust,
and to think on what's right;

To demonstrate kindness
—stay strong, be the light."

And so the three travelers
soon found their way home,
Grateful for each day
they'd gotten to roam.

And now, we invite you to do as we do:
Make connections with nature,
and with others, too.

ABOUT THE BOOK

When Clay said, "Mom, I want to publish a book," it was certainly a joyous day. He originally wanted to write a sequel to Dragons Love Tacos to build off of the book series success. What started as a funny morning conversation turned into a special journey of closeness and connection through many dozens of walks and deep conversations. We are so happy to share this once-in-a-lifetime experience with you!

Please order additional copies and share this book with neighbors, family, and friends. We must share the goodness we find in the world to support kids and adults through their stress, loneliness, overwhelm, and confusion.

Visit TheLongForestTrail.com to experience the power of connection with nature and each other for stronger health and happiness.

ABOUT THE AUTHORS

Clay Vilhauer is a 7-year-old, kind-hearted explorer who lives in Northern Colorado. He wants to be a LEGO® Engineer when he grows up. Playing with family, drawing, all types of sports, and building things are a few of his favorite activities.

Clay was inspired to write this book to teach adults and children to "Be the Light". He believes that by focusing on what you can control—your thoughts (mindset) and feelings inside—you can make the world a happier place.

Co-author Amber Vilhauer will tell you her life's purpose is to help others feel seen, heard, loved, and valued. She is deeply fulfilled in her work, helping impact-driven influencers (both big and small) get their message out to the world in the most powerful way through digital marketing opportunities.

Amber owns and operates multiple brands that support the amplification of author's voices:

- NGNG Enterprises (standing for NoGutsNoGlory!) – An award-winning marketing agency that offers strategic direction for book launches, website design, marketing, monetization, and overall business growth.
- STRONGPrint Publishing – An innovative publishing imprint rooted in giving authors quality, control, and care for their books and other media.
- Books & Business – An education, events, and community platform designed to give entrepreneurs strategy, systems, and speed to scale their online business.

Special thanks to: Illustrator Andres Meneses, Editors Brooke Vitale and Sandra Beck, Proofreader Amy Valentine, and the entire publishing production team at Merack Publishing in collaboration with STRONGPrint Publishing.

Printed in the USA
CPSIA information can be obtained
at www.ICGtesting.com
LVHW070036151123
763986LV00024B/680